45 Year Memorial Photo Album

IROQUOIS
ROLLOUT

JULY 22, 1957

Iroquois Rollout
45 Year Memorial Photo Album
Copyright© 2002, Arrow Alliance Press

Canadian Cataloging in Publication Data

ISBN 1-55056-906-6

Main entry under title:

Arrow Rollout
45 Year Memorial Photo Album
        Includes index.
        ISBN 1-55056-906-6
        1. Arrow...Aviation
        2. Rebuilding...History, Canada
        3. Photo Collection
1.†Avro Arrow (Turbojet fighter plane)--Pictorial works.
I.†Title.
Tl685.3.Z875 2002   623.7'464   C2002-905235-1

First Printing, October 2002

Design by Peter Zuuring & Jozef VanVeenen
Typesetting and Layout by Jozef VanVeenen
Cover Design - Jozef VanVeenen
Photo Editing/Retouching - Jozef VanVeenen
Editing - Essence Communications

Printed and Bound in Canada by Friesens

Contact Us

62 North Street,
Kingston, Ontario K7K 1J8
Phone/Fax: (613) 531-4156
Direct E-mail: arrowz@attcanada.ca
Web E-mail: director@arrow-alliance.com
Website: arrow-alliance.com

The Arrow Alliance and its subsidiaries / affiliates are official licencees of the Canada Aviation Museum in Ottawa. Furthermore the Alliance has permission from Magellan Aerospace Ltd., Malton, for the use of the Avro Aircraft and Orenda Engines logos as well as permission without recourse to use of the photos presented. Even though ownership of the Hawker Siddeley photo negative collection was transferred to the National Aviation Museum in Ottawa, in the early nineteen nineties, any residual copyrights that Magellan Aerospace may have acquired through their acquisition of Orenda Engines Ltd. have been kindly waived and confirmed by our photo reproduction agreement with the Canada Aviation Museum of Ottawa.

Summer 2002

The Story of the Photos

The actual delivery/acceptance document that proves Hawker Siddeley Canada Ltd. transferred ownership of the 14,000+ historical photo collection to the National Aviation Museum, in the early nineties, for a tax receipt and safe keeping.

Early in 2002 I found out that the Canada Aviation Museum in Ottawa had acquired more than 14,000 photo negatives from Hawker Siddeley Canada Ltd. in the early 1990s. These recorded many aspects of the former A.V.Roe Canada Ltd. umbrella organization that included Avro Aircraft Ltd. and Orenda Engines Ltd. They are stored in many small boxes and drawers in several places around the museum.

Some sorting of these negatives had been done by volunteers soon after their acquisition but only in a global way. I became a registered volunteer and got the task of continuing this process. Was I in for a surprise! Day after day I stared, like a Radiologist, at the lightbox - passing my loop over the 4 X 5 inch negative with obvious delight, sometimes boredom, and yes, "Eureka!" at times.

After several months I isolated approximately 3,000 negatives that applied directly to the Avro Arrow and Orenda Iroquois developments. Further sorting into Avro and Orenda, then into development, manufacturing, operating, ceremonial/events, people, and then further subsets of these, led to being able to pick about 360 really superb photos. These photos relate to important events that tie into a 45 year memorial possibility. They are the Arrow's rollout, the Arrow's first flight and the Iroquois' rollout...yes there was an Iroquois rollout celebration, albeit with less fanfare than the Arrow. Many of these were new to me and a delight to behold.

BGM imaging in Ottawa is the designated photo processing house for the museum. After some time/price negotiations with BGM's vice-president Rip Jones, the negatives were supplied in three batches. Paul Latreille , their experienced darkroom man, was assigned to the job. Both BGM and Paul are to be commended for the effort they put into this project. One never knows the quality of the positive that comes from an old negative. Many times several exposures were made in order to balance grey scales and saturations of black and white, so that later computer scanning would have the best possible result. Furthermore, the work was completed in record time.

The quality of BGM's work coupled with the photo retouching skills of Joe VanVeenen, our Graphic Designer, gives you these wonderful snapshots of an unforgettable period in our aviation history.

Peter Zuuring,
Kingston, ON, Fall 2002

A stripped down MK II Iroquois flies through the air with the greatest of ease, in this often used publicity shot.

Introduction

It is with great pleasure that I present this Limited Edition 45 Year Memorial Photo Album of the Iroquois Rollout for your viewing pleasure.

I have been digging out the Arrow / Iroquois story for five years. Along the way I have found amazing things and met many fantastic Canadians some of whom had the honour and thrill of working at Avro or Orenda directly during those heady days in Malton. Finding the photos that you are about to peruse has been particularly delightful. Orenda's photo crew did a superb job. Their efforts look as fresh today as they did then.

Many people are unaware that Orenda's Iroquois jet engine had its days of public glory too. Albeit not as big an event as the Arrow's rollout, it was significant, and perhaps a more formal affair. Several hundred invited guests, including the usual military, government and foreign attaches were there. The Orenda Pipe Band gathered on the front lawn of Orenda's Plant#2, and kicked off the ceremony. Invitees were asked to take their seat in the large Rollout tent setup for the event. Company executives guided VIP guests to the platform. Speeches by Walter McLachlan, Orenda President and General Manager; Air Marshall Slemon, Chief of the Air Staff; and George Pearkes, Minister of National Defence, followed the same format as that of the Arrow's Rollout ceremony to come, several months later.

Once the unveiling was complete, the visiting started in earnest, as everyone wandered over to the other large refreshment tent, all decked out for the occasion.

One of the Iroquois high pressure compressor assemblies - hub and blading. A piece of art just by itself. Building #7 the NRC engine test facility, Ottawa, Montreal Road campus, has a similar assembly above its receiving door.

The Iroquois really was a marvel. It was the lightest weight and corresponding thrust jet turbine in the world. It went through several iterations in record time. The MKII version was the third of its type, and could have pushed the Arrow to its design limit of about mach # 2.3 at which point skin temperatures are over 250 degrees. Any higher friction built up temperature would weaken the aluminum frame—this barrier was called the thermal thicket.

A licencing deal was in the works with Curtis-Wright of the USA, the French wanted the engine for the Mirage, and we needed the Iroquois for the Arrow...derated, non-afterburning, versions could have been sold into the new commercial jet market...what a future.

This photo record, that you are about to see, gives a small glimpse into the making of one of Canada's most daring aerospace ventures, which in the end didn't see the light of day!

Plant #1 is getting a facelift by applying the Orenda name and logo. Today, the building is the International Centre. People walk the hall and have no idea that this was the home of the Iroquois.

Charles Grinyer - Orenda's Vice-President of Engineering

"There is one member of the Orenda team who merits special mention today."...W. McLachlan speaks to the VIP's during the Iroquois' Rollout.

Charles Grinyer, like Jim Floyd of Avro, was the man of the hour. His guidance and drive produced the Iroquois. He was respected and a man of principal. He told me the Iroquois program was a nasty business from the beginning. How could this be?

Charles explained that from the beginning of the project, the Government wanted in on everything. All details of the design and production were open to scrutiny. Orenda had a hard time keeping manufacturing techniques and metallurgical details confidential. Groundbreaking work on the use of lightweight titanium was a crucial part of the Iroquois design. No one wanted the competition to have an edge in this strategic material for engine or airframe use. Charles told me that Orenda would accept contracts from Atomic Energy of Canada. They actually had nothing to do with anything but the Iroquois' development —to keep the Department of Defence Production out of the loop.

In this memorial photo album, you will follow the manufacture of the MKI and MKII Iroquois, through its public unveiling, into flight test with the B47, and over to Avro for test fitting into the MKII Arrow RL206. We conclude with a great

opportunity lost, in cancelling this jewel of the whole Avro Arrow project. Just one licencee, Curtis-Wright, thought they could have sold about 12,000 Iroquois engines into various military and commercial applications over the life of the project. It was worth millions of dollars, and we let it slip away!

Many able people worked on this technical achievement. Harry Keast, Orenda's Chief Engineer; Burt Avery, Chief Design Engineer; and Syd Britton, Chief Administrative Engineer; to name a few, along with hundreds of dedicated Orenda employees, made it happen. The overall impression created by the Orenda Engines team, was that they were an aggressive, intelligent and imaginative group, with a sound approach to engineering design and manufacturing skill.

Charles Grinyer strikes a classic pose in this official Orenda photo. He was committed to his job. Although he could be tough, his enthusiasm infected those around him.

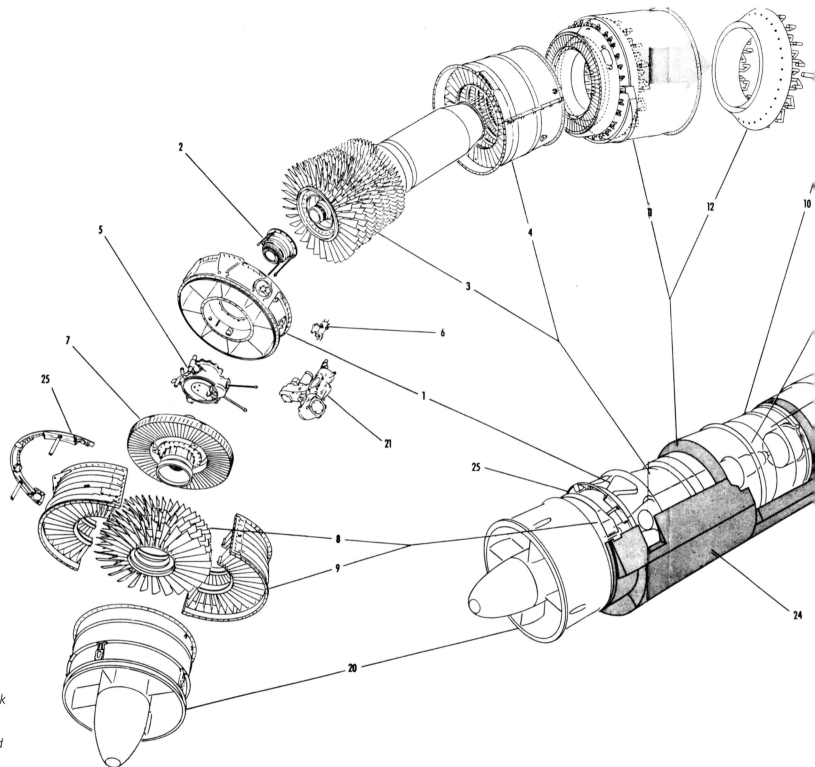

A major component expansion of the Iroquois shows how it is assembled. Look closely at this major parts drawing. You will be able to recognize various pieces, as you see the Iroquois being assembled through the next few pages.

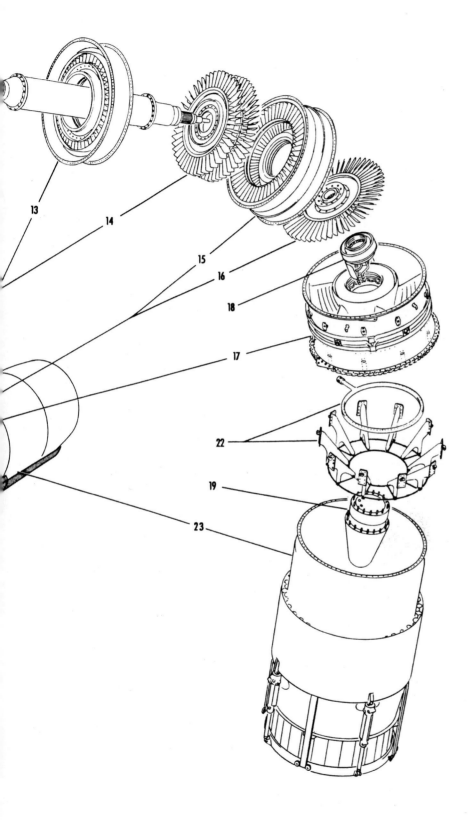

	83000	General Assembly - Engine
- 1	85510	Frame Assembly - Front
- 2	82830	Bearing Assembly - HP thrust
- 3	84300	Rotor Assembly - HP compressor
- 4	84370	Stator Assembly - HP compressor
- 5	84820	Gearbox and Oil Tank Assembly - Internal
- 6	84830	Gearbox Assembly - LP external
- 7	85520	Bearing Assembly - LP thrust
- 8	84420	Rotor Assembly - LP compressor
- 9	84230	Stator Assembly - LP compressor
-10	82950	Shaft Assembly - LP main
-11	83960	Frame Assembly - Mid
-12	85210	Plate Assembly - Combustion base
-13	84460	Stator Assembly - Turbine front
-14	84450	Rotor Assembly - HP turbine
-15	84470	Stator Assembly - Turbine rear
-16	84760	Rotor Assembly - LP turbine
-17	85080	Frame Assembly - Rear
-18	85380	Bearing Assembly - Turbine
-19	85370	Bullet Assembly - Rear frame
-20	85050	Frame Assembly - Inlet
-21	84910	Gearbox Assembly - HP external and aircraft power take-off
-22	85420	Spray Rings and Stabilizers - Afterburner
-23	83710	Afterburner Assembly
-24	84200	Engine Firewall Arrangement
-25		Restrictor - Nacelle air
	85300	Systems Arrangement
	85400	External Components and Bolting Arrangement
	80600	Installation - Engine

MK I Iroquois are being assembled in the recently revamped Orenda Plant # 1, today the International Centre, across Airport road from Avro. The two stage low pressure turbine is being positioned in place. Note the fuel pipe inlets surrounding the annular combustion chamber.

Looking the other way, down the Iroquois assembly line. The high pressure central rotor has been installed. The whole engine could be lowered into the floor and worked on at eye level for ease of access.

The first assembled MK I Iroquois is on the hoist, left and right side views are shown.

The completed Iroquois MK I, 50 hour test engine en route to the test cells.

The 50 hour MK I test engine arrives at the new test cells—it is fully instrumented. It would be used on the B47 flying test bed later on. This is the engine that found its way to the Canadian Warplane Heritage Museum via an airline pilot's tax receipt, MacEwen wreckers in Moncton and the NRC after the program was cancelled.

The same engine being hoisted and mounted in the test cell, ready for that all important 50 hour test, a major milestone in any engine development.

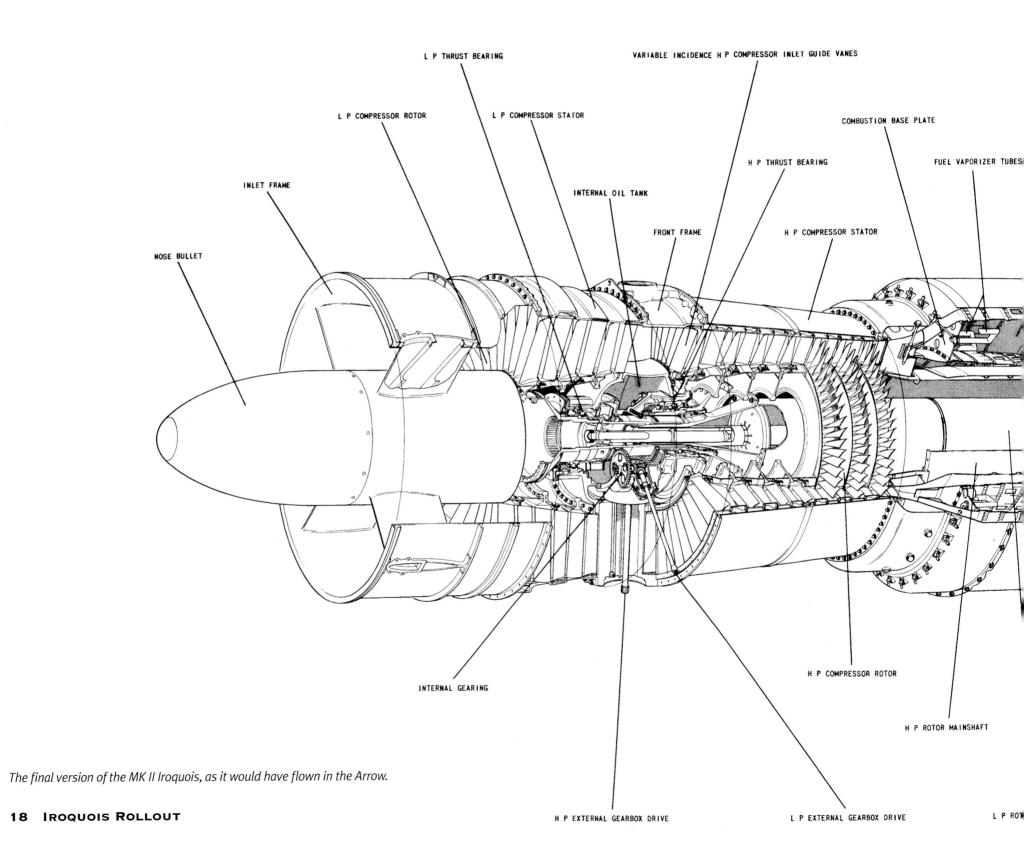

LP THRUST BEARING

VARIABLE INCIDENCE H P COMPRESSOR INLET GUIDE VANES

LP COMPRESSOR ROTOR

L P COMPRESSOR STATOR

COMBUSTION BASE PLATE

INLET FRAME

INTERNAL OIL TANK

H P THRUST BEARING

FUEL VAPORIZER TUBES

NOSE BULLET

FRONT FRAME

H P COMPRESSOR STATOR

INTERNAL GEARING

H P COMPRESSOR ROTOR

H P ROTOR MAINSHAFT

The final version of the MK II Iroquois, as it would have flown in the Arrow.

H P EXTERNAL GEARBOX DRIVE

L P EXTERNAL GEARBOX DRIVE

L P ROT

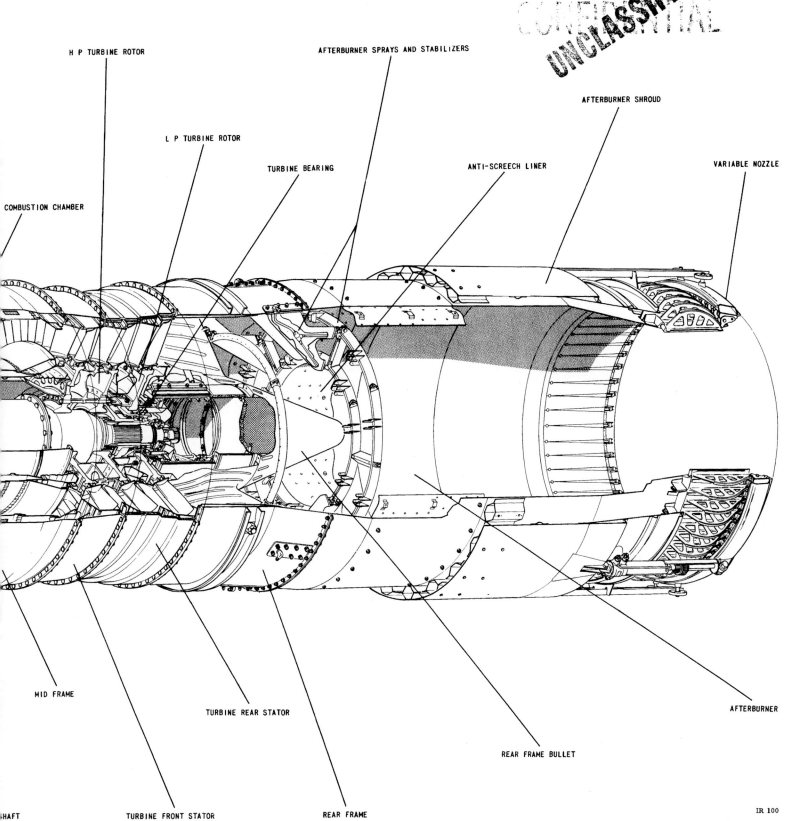

H P TURBINE ROTOR

L P TURBINE ROTOR

TURBINE BEARING

AFTERBURNER SPRAYS AND STABILIZERS

AFTERBURNER SHROUD

ANTI-SCREECH LINER

VARIABLE NOZZLE

COMBUSTION CHAMBER

MID FRAME

TURBINE REAR STATOR

AFTERBURNER

HAFT

TURBINE FRONT STATOR

REAR FRAME

REAR FRAME BULLET

IR 100

The high pressure compressor and turbine assembly is assembled as one unit. There were two rotors , one inside the other. The inner one was the low pressure, 3 stage, compressor and single stage turbine, while the high pressure, 7 stage, compressor and double stage high pressure turbine was on the outside. This test rig checked the rigidity of the outer assembly.

Mk II Iroquois engines in assembly. The MK II was more powerful, (MK II meant Mac 2 capable). Some of these differences were, from the front: the bullet nose was more stream-lined, the inlet supports were central as apposed to tangential, and in between the low and high pressure compressors there was a variable pitch blade assembly to control rotational stall.

The walking stick ejectors and fuel delivery to the annular combustion chamber was more efficient, the afterburner incorporated redesigned gutters and spray bars, as well as an improved screech plate design to prevent excessive vibrations and sonic shocks, the guts of the motor were encased in a flame proof shroud, and deflecting attachments around the engine channeled air around it to control cooling.

After each run the engine was generally stripped down and inspected. Walking stick fuel inlets reversed the flow to vapourize as much of the JP4 as possible before igniting. The photo shows this didn't always work as planned. The crud that builds up in the annular combustion chamber is amazing.

A MK II Iroquois is on the assembly cart. The rings, at either end, were attached on the actual engine mounts. Working on any part of the engine was easy. We are looking at the bottom side. From the left, the square box, on the side, is the ignition system, the pressure bottle contains oxygen for the patented high altitude ignition system; the angle conical piece is the attachment end of the auxiliary gear box, which would attach to the Arrow fuel/hydraulic pumps; all those pipes, to the right, hide the Lucas fuel flow control unit, the afterburner control unit, and many more hydraulic /fuel feed back devices. All neatly bundled and compact.

Installing the afterburner spray ring.

Do you have the right drawing?

A great view of the new test cells, constructed for the Arrow/Iroquois program; they lasted for years.

The MK II Iroquois is tested in one of the new cells...the pictures are self explanatory. Everybody in the neighborhood knew when the Iroquois was under test...it roared for miles and gave off the tell-tale white plum of condensed steam.

*The little indent , about halfway down the length of the engine, is where the throttle cable assembly is attached.
There is an opposite like connection on the other side.*

Hundreds of connections for pressure, temperature, flow rates, vibration, accelerometers, etc...all this sensor output data was piped into the common control area between any two cells.

The head-on view of the MKII Iroquois. The coil and small pipe at the base of the inlet cowling sensed icing conditions. If icing was detected, a hot air feed from the 10th stage high pressure compressor, through a flapper valve, distributed this heated air back to the front support struts, bullet nose, and first stage stator blades, which were hollow.

Everybody living near the Orenda plant heard the roar of the Iroquois as a test run got underway.

Charles Grinyer, Orenda's Vice-President of Engineering, explains the complexities of jet engine manufacture to Prince Bernard of the Netherlands. Earle Brownridge, Orenda's Executive Vice-President and General Manager looks on behind the Prince's back.

A section of the Iroquois display engine arrives, is taken out of its protective shipping crate, and assembled with the other parts as shown in the following photos—ready for the official unveiling ceremony on Monday, July 22, 1957.

Curiously enough Orenda used on MKI assembly for their show engine. It was the older technology. Maybe nobody noticed or maybe it was done on purpose, after all the Iroquois was still in development.

The Iroquois display engine sits on the guest parking lot walkway of Orenda of Derry Road West. The night before the rollout ceremony, the engine is positioned and draped by plant personnel. Two large tents, one for the ceremony and the other for the official reception afterwards, are erected on the Orenda, Plant #2, front lawn.

Setting up the display in the reception tent continued through Sunday evening.

This is the day, Monday July 22, 1957. A covered walkway guides VIPs to the unveiling tent. Mrs. Earle Brownridge smiles at her husband.

More VIPs and platform guests arrive for the Iroquois unveiling. Just visible to the left are John Pallett, M.P. for Peel; Nathan Phillips, Toronto's Mayor; and Roland Michener, M.P. for St.Paul.

Platform dignitaries are arriving—from left to right;Air Marshall, C.R. Slemon, Chief of the Air Staff, RCAF; John Tory, QC, Member of the Board A.V. Roe Canada Ltd.; Fred Smye, Executive Vice-President, A.V. Roe Canada Ltd.; Wilf Curtis, Vice Chairman, Board of Directors, A.V. Roe Canada Ltd.; Walter R. McLachlan, President, Orenda Engines Ltd.

The Defence Minister, George C. Pearkes, VC, is greeted by Earle Brownridge, on the left and Walter McLachlan, both introduced earlier.

Defence Minister, George C. Pearkes, VC, is shown chatting with Marg Fry (Centre), Experimental Purchasing Department; and Doly Ford, of Production Control.

Among the attendees were various military attaches from the UK, USA, France, Germany and Turkey.

Walter McLachlan makes the opening address for the assembled VIPs. The still veiled Iroquois is shown on the left.

Design of Iroquois Great Stimulus for Young Canadians

Walter R. McLachlan's speech as reported in "The Orenda," Volume 3, Number 14, July 26, 1957

Orenda President and General Manager Walter R. McLachlan, speaking before an impressive array of guests at the official unveiling of the Iroquois last Monday, said that a challenge such as the design and production of the Iroquois engine is a terrific stimulus to brilliant young Canadians.

"If we can tackle and succeed in a task like this, involving very advanced thinking in physics, metallurgy, electronics and mechanical design, we do not need to say we can't design in Canada," said Mr. McLachlan.

"For years we have been exporting many of our best brains from Canada, for lack of opportunity to use their talents in this country," he said. "This has been changing—we are becoming recognized in our own right in the fields of medicine, mining, agriculture, civil engineering and law. It is only very recently that it has been recognized that we are competent in the field of mechanical design and even more recently that we can make a contribution in the field of aeronautical engineering."

He told the audience of guests from fields of government, education, armed forces, industry and labor that many students come to Orenda Engines Limited to see the work carried on—and are encouraged by what their fellow Canadians are doing.

"The Iroquois engine that you see here today is the result of the finest type of team work," said Mr. McLachlan.

He said that today we have a largely integrated aero engine industry in Canada, and, as an example, the Orenda which powers the Sabre and CF-100 is 95 percent Canadian content.

"Most important to any industrial organization is the partners who supply the specialized equipment and services, and we are happy that so many of our suppliers are represented here today," said the Orenda President.

"The little fellow that started all this was the Chinook—the first jet engine to be designed and built in Canada. The thinking behind this was started by National Research Council and a Crown Company called Turbo Research in the early forties. At the end of the war, most of the scientists and engineers engaged on this work joined A. V. Roe Canada, and in March, 1948, the Chinook delivered power—the first jet engine to be designed and built in Canada.

Flew in Sabre

"From this original work came the Orenda, then a very advanced concept in terms of power. It flew in a Sabre aircraft in 1950. The Orenda developed almost three times the power of its predecessor, the Chinook, and the next step forward represented by the Iroquois will triple the power of the Orenda. Most significant is the reduction in weight represented by this new engine.

"The Chinook gave one and a half pounds of thrust for each pound of engine weight—the Orenda three pounds—and the Iroquois over five pounds. So rapid has been the technical development that in seven years the Iroquois can give nearly four times the power for each pound of metal used in the engine. This is of paramount importance to the aircraft designer —since every pound taken out of the engine means about four pounds taken out of the airframe."

The Iroquois weighs less per pound of thrust than any other large supersonic engine known to be running to date.

"There are two very significant points which flow from this Canadian development—apart from the defence aspect," said Mr. McLachlan. "The first is the impetus which stems from this work into commercial development. Let me give you an example—the metal titanium. This is a very interesting metal. It has the same strength as steel for only 60 percent of the weight. It has high resistance to corrosion, hence it is of great interest to the chemical industry, the transport industry and the shipbuilders.

200 Tons of Ore

"I am told that in one area in Quebec we have more than 200 million tons of titanium ore. At present it is too expensive for general commercial use, but its use in aircraft and aero engines is justified due to the saving in weight. It is possible that in time it will find its proper place, as aluminum has done—and provide a new basic industry in Canada. The development work done on the Iroquois has proved to us that it is a sound engineering material, and can be forged, machined and welded in quantity."

He said the second point which flows from this Canadian development concerns people, and went on to describe how Orenda, by showing what Canadians can do in the design field, is contributing to the future development of this country.

"It is not possible to mention all the Orenda people who have worked on the Iroquois project," said Mr. McLachlan, "but they are represented here today by the senior officials of The Orenda Professional Engineers Association, The International Association of Machinists and The Orenda Management.

Special Merit

"There is one member of the Orenda team who merits special mention today. This man has organized and led this project in a completely devoted spirit. His initiative, courage and technical foresight have been an inspiration to all of us who have been associated with the Iroquois project. I refer to Charles Grinyer, our Vice-President of Engineering at Orenda."

He said there were many people outside Orenda who have contributed to this effort, and named: the technical officers of the RCAF; the National Aeronautical Establishment at Ottawa; the universities—particularly the Institute of Aerophysics of the University of Toronto; the Department of Mines and Technical Surveys, on metallurgical problems; the Government

Air Marshall C. R. Slemon, Chief of the Air Staff, RCAF, speaks about the role of the Iroquois in North American defence.

agencies in U.K. and U.S.A. who have collaborated with us in exchange of basic research data; and our colleagues in Avro Aircraft.

2,100 Suppliers

"If I have forgotten anyone, it is because we have had so much genuine interest expressed by those struggling with similar problems," said Mr. McLachlan. "I spoke previously about the contribution made by our supporting industry, and I should like again to stress the importance of this. There are more than 2,100 firms who supply Orenda with materials, components and services. While much of the work has been done in Canada, our friends in the U.K. and U.S. have been extremely interested in our work and have assisted us in many ways."

He mentioned that the Iroquois would be in Washington from July 31 to August 4 and in Britain for the Farnborough Air Show during September.

Significant Milestone

Air Marshal C. R. Slemon's speech as reported in "The Orenda," Volume 3, Number 14, July 26, 1957

Air Marshal C. R. Slemon, Chief of Air Staff, speaking on behalf of the RCAF at the official unveiling of the Iroquois engine last Monday, said the Iroquois would keep Canada's weapons system abreast of defence requirements. He also made some observations on the future character of defence.

He said the Orenda powers the CF-100s up to altitudes of eight or nine miles above earth in something like seven or eight minutes. Compared with the CF-100, the next all-weather interceptor, the "Avro, Arrow", will weigh twice as much, but the Iroquois engine will power it to altitudes four or five miles higher; it will get up there in about half the time and it will fly it better than twice the speed, said Air Marshal Slemon.

Keep Abreast

"Furthermore, the potential of the Iroquois is such as will enable it to be developed to powers considerably in excess of the first versions of the engine," he said. "This is highly important in our constant efforts to keep abreast of the threat posed by the increasing performance of the weapons which could be launched against North America.

"We can expect the threat to include guided missiles in due course. Nevertheless, bombers will continue to comprise a significant part of the threat for or as long as we can foresee and, therefore, for this and other reasons, manned interceptors will continue as an essential element of our defences—thus the importance of the Iroquois engine. Confidence in his weapons and equipment is mighty important to the fighting man. We have confidence in this Iroquois engine because the team responsible for the success of its forerunners is still on the job."

Proud of Fighters

"The small brother of this big jet engine is the Orenda, which powers our CF-100 all-weather interceptors. These interceptors, of which we are rightly proud, are the product of Avro Aircraft Limited in the factory adjoining this one. The Orenda also powers our F-86 Sabres, our day interceptors made by Canadair Limited of Montreal, of which we are equally proud," he said. "That these three Canadian companies and their sub-contractors have worked so effectively together in producing fighter machines of such great excellence is a matter of real pride for every Canadian who thinks seriously about the security of our country."

Finally George Pearkes, Minister of National Defence, has the honour and pleasure of unveiling the Iroquois engine. The ceremony is more toned down and formal, compared to the extravaganza planned for the Arrow's rollout.

Outstanding Technical Achievement

George R. Pearkes's speech as reported in "The Orenda," Volume 3, Number 14, July 26, 1957

Defence Minister George R. Pearkes, VC, paid high tribute to the outstanding technical achievement made by—Orenda Engines Limited—in' the design of its new supersonic jet interceptor, the Iroquois, at the official unveiling ceremonies held on the front lawn of Plant 2 last Monday.

"The Iroquois has attracted attention from all over the world," Mr. Pearkes said. "It is remarkable that a country so new to the exacting and complex scientific engineering field has produced an aero engine of such advanced design and performance in such a short span of time.

"The jet engine we are unveiling today represents an outstanding technical achievement for the aviation and defence industry of Canada," Mr. Pearkes added. "Its development was a courageous step forward, as it involved many unsolved, difficult and intricate problems inherent in such an advanced design."

Achieve Lightness

One such problem, for example, was the machining and welding of the new titanium alloys to achieve the lightness of weight which is so important and such an outstanding feature of this high thrust engine, he added.

"The scientific skills of the development and production staffs accumulated in Canada during the development and production of the Chinook and Orenda engines, have contributed in great measure to overcoming the prob lems of this supersonic jet engine design," the Defence Minister told the 250 guests at the special ceremony on the lawn of Plant 2.

Powerful Engine

The Iroquois is one of the most powerful and advanced jet engines of today. The potential development of the engine will provide more thrust than any other engine in the same stage of development. The magnitude of the Iroquois power can perhaps be visualized by realizing that during four minutes of high speed flight, it will consume more fuel than is required to operate the average automobile for one year.

Contribute Greatly

Mr. Pearkes said he felt it was important to mention that the design and development teams associated with the Chinook, Orenda and Iroquois have not only incorporated their considerable technical knowledge into the production of these engines, but they have also contributed significantly to the fields of aerodynamic and metallurgical sciences in Canada generally.

"This development of Canadian technology is significant because a country's defence capabilities are becoming increasingly and inescapably dependant on the industrial capacity which it possesses," he said. "It is true that Canadian industrial development has been a potent factor f or many years, and there can be no question of the important part played by Canadian industry during the Second World War.

Build Up Research

"Nevertheless, the degree of dependance by the Armed Services on industry has increased tremendously throughout the last decade. This responsibility which Canadian industry has inherited makes it imperative that industry build up research and design facilities, in collaboration with the responsible government agencies, because these facilities are essential for the development and production of weapons and equipment for the defence forces.

"The tremendous strides made by Canadian industry over the past few years are most en couraging. They have shown through achievements such as the Iroquois—that its capabilities in various fields continues to develop and expand. Furthermore, our increasing technological resources have also enabled us to assist other countries, who share our strong beliefs in the values of life, to increase their defence preparedness.

War Deterrant

"A notable example in this regard is the provision to many countries, through our Mutual Aid program and sales, of large numbers of Canadian-built Sabre fighters and CF-100 interceptors, powered by Orenda jet engines. It is no exaggeration to say that Canada's part in contributing to the strength of our NATO partnership is a substantial factor in maintaining an effective war deterrant.

"Our whole defence program must, of course, be worked out in close collaboration with our allies to prevent unnecessary and costly duplication, and to ensure as far as possible that our efforts and those of our allies are programmed to achieve maximum effectiveness with greatest possible economy."

Defence Posture

He said that such a course of action would go far towards creating a defence posture aimed as a deterrant to future war.

"In our search for new horizons and the translation of new concepts into producible and practical defence equipment, we have working on our behalf the scientists of the Defence Research Board, the technical consultants of other government departments, the technical officers of the services and the great body- of private industry, one of whose products we see here today. Therefore, in this Iroquois engine we see demonstrated that Orenda Engines Limited and their associates are indeed a vital part of the great defence team. I congratulate everyone who has contributed to this achievement.

Unveils Iroquois

"I now have great pleasure in unveiling the supersonic jet j engine —the Iroquois"! With this remark, the cover was lifted from the Iroquois model. Mr. Pearkes then shook the hands with the two Orenda girls who lifted the cover—Marg Fry, Experimental Purchasing Department, and Dolly Ford, Production Control Department—and inspected the engine, which is designed to power Canada's top twin-engine supersonic interceptor, the Avro Arrow.

As the cover is rolled back, the gleaming, stripped down, display Iroquois is formally revealed. Orenda hostesses flank each end.

Orenda employees, Dolly and Marg pose in front of the unveiled Iroquois.

George Pearkes takes the opportunity to congratulate and thank Dolly Ford for her presence.

IROQUOIS
THRUST - over 20,000 lbs.
WEIGHT - classified

THE FIRST SUPERSONIC TURBOJET DESIGNED AND DEVELOPED IN
CANADA, ONE OF THE MOST ADVANCED TURBOJET ENGINES IN THE
WORLD, HAVING AN EXCEPTIONAL THRUST-WEIGHT RATIO, NOTABLE
FOR ITS SIMPLICITY OF DESIGN AND THE USE OF NEW ENGINEER-
ING CONCEPTS AND ENGINEERING MATERIALS, PARTICULARLY TITANIUM.
PRODUCTION ENGINES WILL POWER THE AVRO AIRCRAFT
ARROW SUPERSONIC INTERCEPTOR NOW UNDER DEVELOPMENT.

THE
IROQUOIS
DESIGNED AND MANUFACTURED
IN CANADA BY
ORENDA ENGINES LIMITED

Roy Slemon, George Pearkes and Walter McLachlan pose for the official photos.

An interesting cameo shot of some of the platform guests...they must have cracked a joke because everyone is beaming... is it the Iroquois or the girls... I'll leave this to you!
From the left: Dolly Ford, George Pearkes, Marg Fry, Roy Slemon, Walter McLachlan, Roland Michener, Fred Smye and Ozzie Waffle, Reeve of Etobicoke Township.

THE IROQUOIS

DESIGNED AND MANUFACTURED ... BY ... NES LIMITED

Air Attaches from left to right, A/C, B.J. R. Roberts, UK; Col. R.H. Jones, USA; Major C. Orhun, Turkey; Col F.C. Schlichting, West Germany; and Col A.R. Deperrois, France.

The crowd now has a chance to mingle, chat and view the Iroquois at their leisure.

John B. Hamilton, Member of Parliament for York West, looks over his shoulder, with George Pearkes close behind.

Another fun shot. Dolly and Marg are having a good time posing for the camera.

The nose of the Iroquois seems to be a natural gathering spot. Ozzie Waffle is revealing all he doesn't know about the Iroquois. Reeve Mary Fix of Toronto Township and Mayor Nathan Phillips listen with interest while Charles Grinyer, Orenda's Vice-President of Engineering and Chief Engineer, stands by to lend a helping hand!

Earlier in the day, the Orenda Pipe Band kicked off the Ceremonies. Later, the Bandmaster lends his hat to Dolly Ford who appears to be somewhat more self-conscious than Marg Fry.

Official guests are treated to a light snack after the ceremony in a separate tent. More time to visit and catch up with the gossip of the day!

Roland Michener caught up in the fray. What a different affair from the Arrow's rollout.

George Pearkes has a few words to say. No doubt he is discussing the implication of the use of titanium in the Iroquois on the world supply of this strategic material.

The B47, a big multi-jet bomber on loan to Orenda and the Arrow program from the USAF, arrives at Malton. It was modified to carry the Iroquois and associated test equipment by Canadair in Montreal. Tricky flying to say the least.

The Boeing has landed and has been parked in Avro's south-west staging area. The press have been invited, as well as the usual assortment of Orenda and Avro staff and a few models to boot.

Looking east, under the belly of the plane, Len Hobbs, co-pilot, on the left, and Johnny MacLaughlin, flight engineer, have just come out and are greeted by Public Relations staff.

As Mike Cooper-Slipper, Chief Test Pilot, descends the ladder, a more formal photo op presents itself.

A touching photo, as Mike and his wife kiss with passion upon his arrival. His young son looks on with interest. Obviously a happy relieved family! The take-off from Montreal's Cartierville airport was difficult, because there would be no second chance.

A great view into the throat of the Iroquois mounted on the right side of the B47 in a long nacelle. To prevent early wind-milling of the engine in flight, a clam shell cover assembly preceded the inlet of the motor (shown removed). This could be opened in flight when tests were to be carried out.

The first Iroquois has been installed in the pod. Note the reduced complexity, compared to later pictures, as various versions of the engine are test flown.

Look at all that instrumentation. Like the Arrow's weapons pack, the B47 bomb bay was also modified by Canadair to hold recording instruments. It came out like a large folding shelf on the starboard side of the plane just in front of the Iroquois.

Closer still—the rear mounting linkage is clearly visible. It centred on the rear bearing assembly.

Len Hobbs and Mike Cooper-Slipper study the flight manuals that came with the B47. An appropriate photo adorns the office wall.

The B47 is pushed back into the main Avro flight line—preparing for another flight. An Arrow parked on the flight line beside it is fitting testimony to a future mating with the Iroquois.

Push back is nearly complete. Special heavy weight handling equipment was needed to push the big bird around.

Len Hobbs, John McLaughlin and Mike Cooper-Slipper pose in front of the B47, ready for another flight with the mighty Iroquois. More than thirty flying hours were logged during this stage of the engine's development. Note the closed clam-shell cover on the Iroquois pod inlet nacelle.

Orenda line crew pay close attention as the B47 is being positioned for another test flight.

Len Hobbs is doing his walk around prior to the next test flight. What a great view of the cockpit. The flight engineer sat below the pilot in the hold.

The walk around complete, Len Hobbs gets ready to come aboard.

Engine start is underway—another flight test is in progress.

A great shot of the B47 and its pilot Mike Cooper-Slipper. It was designated as CL-52 (XO59 experimental), while under the Orenda/RCAF loan arrangement from the USAF.

The single Iroquois could push the B47 along quite on its own. It was so powerful that full off-set thrust of the outer port engine was needed to keep the plane straight. Imagine, the Iroquois was positioned only a few feet off the fuselage centre line.

The future appeared bright for the Iroquois. Lots of money was spent on experimental equipment, not the least of which was The High Altitude Test Facility. This state of the art installation could simulate high altitude flight up to 100,000 feet, including high speed air flows, densities and temperatures.

It was completed at the end of the program, and immediately moth-balled, only to be sold some time later. Crown Asset Disposal Corporation records are unclear about what happened.

The large test chamber shows an Orenda engine undergoing its paces. Before tackling the larger Iroquois, trials with the well known Orenda tested all the facility systems. Note how the large caisson was split and could be wheeled back to open the test chamber cavity.

Iroquois X116 has been wheeled over to the end of Bay #1 production line. In the forefront, for this official photo, is the J-67, one of three, that would power the Avrocar flying saucer.

Iroquois X116 has arrived at the rear of Arrow RL206, parked at the end of the production line, in Bay #1. Once again details are reviewed, before the engine is mounted on its insertion dolly, and cranked into the Arrow's engine bay.

X116 has been mounted on its insertion dolly. Once the pitch and linearity have been aligned with the engine bay support tracking, it can be slowly cranked into position and mounted. In squadron operation Arrow, engine turn around time was specified not to exceed 30 minutes.

The Iroquois is finally mated with the Arrow. It wasn't all roses however, as a number of attachments didn't quite fit. Some felt that the timing of this trial was to placate the RCAF—to show some progress in getting the MKII Arrow closer to completion. Only one Iroquois, X116, ever made it to Avro.

X-116, after the program has been cancelled. It is orphaned at Avro, put back on the Orenda doly, and sits around until it is loaned to Bristol Siddeley of the UK. It was studied to death, helped in evolving the Olympus for TSR2 and Concord, used as a teaching aid at Cranfield College, and finally put to rest, in pieces, in the RAF Hendon Museum storage facility. Why did Avro have their own doly when a perfectly good doly came with the engine from Orenda? Was this part of the higher cost debate?

Opportunity Lost

To sell the Iroquois to the USAF and other US based commercial applications Avro recognized the need for a US based licencee partner. Pratt had their J75 - GE was working on their own development—that left Curtis Wright, a third level supplier, but neutral at least. A licensing deal was signed in 1957. To kick it into action the engine must have first passed the 150 hour final test...it never got the chance to do so before cancellation. In 1956 the Curtis sales team was busy checking the potential sales of the Iroquois through its various incarnations before signing the deal. They estimated that, over the life of the Iroquois, more than 12,000 motors could be sold. This was worth billions of dollars....much more than any sale of the Arrow might have brought in.